we've got the
whole world
in our hands

To the healing hands of Dr. Peter Newton

WE'VE GOT THE WHOLE WORLD IN OUR HANDS

RAFAEL LÓPEZ

SCHOLASTIC INC.

We've got the whole world in our hands.
We've got the whole world in our hands.

We've got you and you've got me in our hands!
We've got the whole world in our hands.

We've got the sun and the rain
in our hands.

We've got the moon and the stars
in our hands.

We've got the whole world
in our hands.

We've got the wind and the clouds in our hands!
We've got the whole world in our hands.

We've got the rivers and the mountains in our hands.

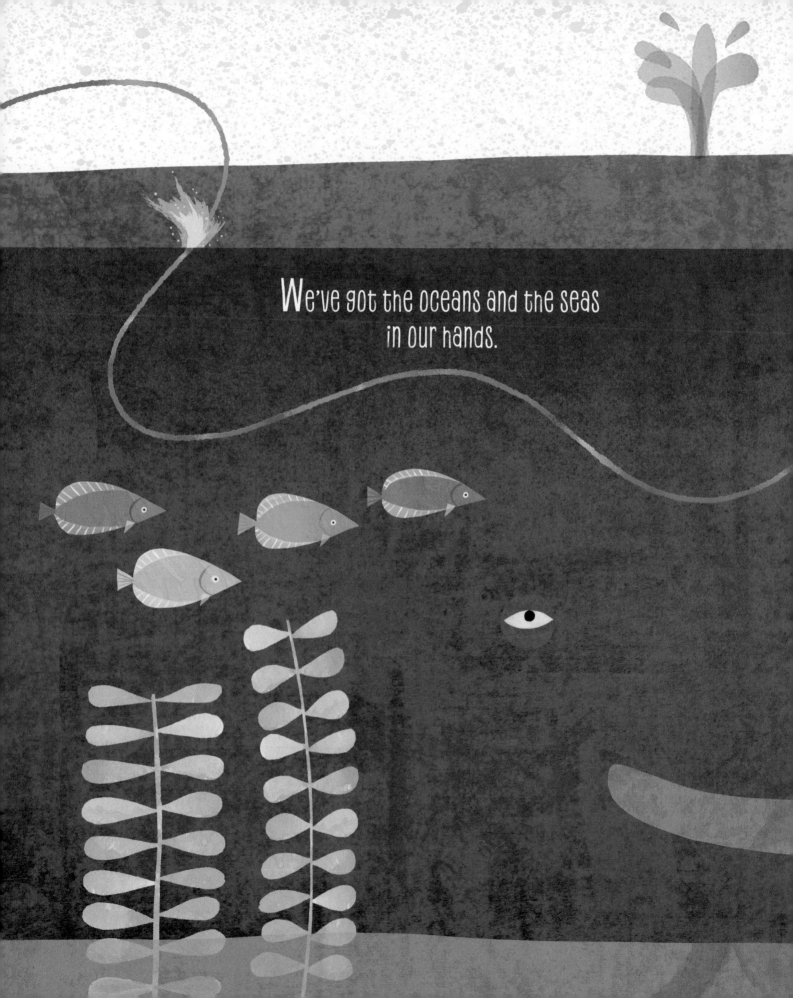

We've got the oceans and the seas in our hands.

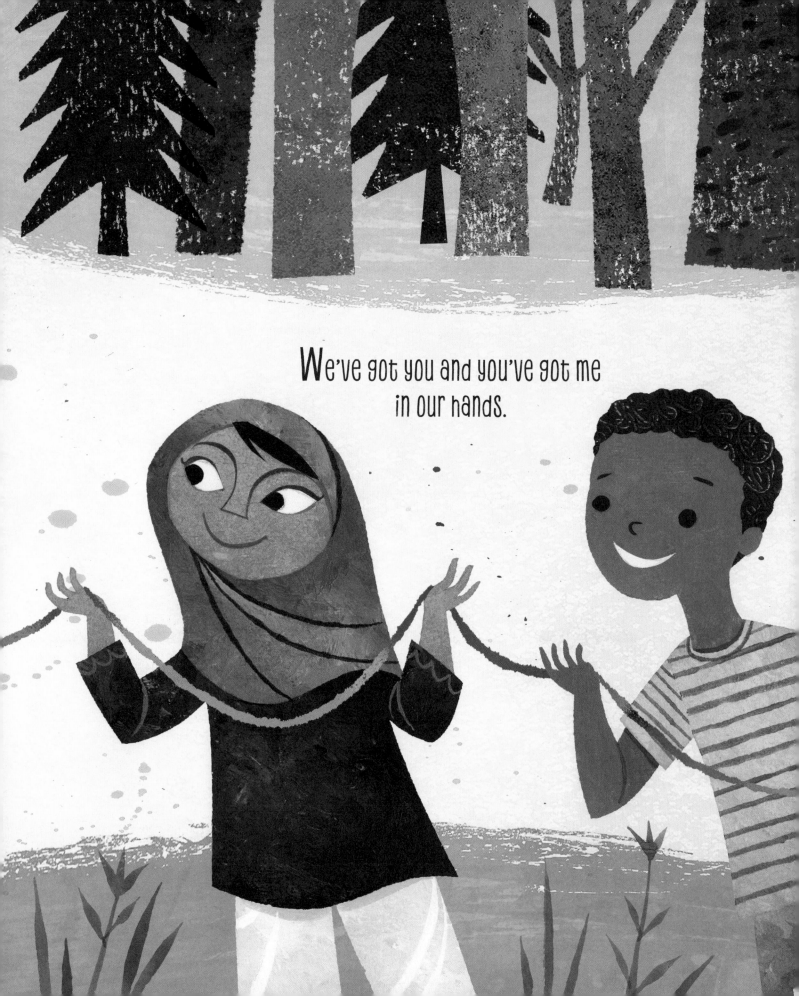

We've got you and you've got me
in our hands.

We've got the whole world
in our hands.

We've got everybody here
in our hands.

We've got the whole world
in our hands.

We've got everybody everywhere in our hands.

We've got the whole world in our hands.

We've got the whole world
in our hands.

We've got the whole world in our hands

About "He's Got the Whole World in His Hands"

The origin of "He's Got the Whole World in His Hands" is uncertain,
but this well-known spiritual has brought joy and hope to people
around the world. The song was first published in a hymnal in 1927.
Since that time, it has been rearranged and sung by many celebrated artists,
including Marian Anderson, Mahalia Jackson, Laurie London, Reverend F.W. McGee,
Odetta, and Nina Simone. The verses have been modified,
but the message of unity has prevailed.

The Artist's Inspiration

Rafael López loves color because it speaks all languages. He uses an array of hues
that come in large recycled salsa jars from Mexico, along with mixed media.
Using his collection of tools and twigs, he scratches texture on the
illustrated surface of wooden boards and watercolor paper. With his
favorite pair of scissors, he cuts shapes out of Bristol paper and then plays with pen
and ink, watercolor, and Adobe Photoshop to conjure the personalities
of clouds and characters.

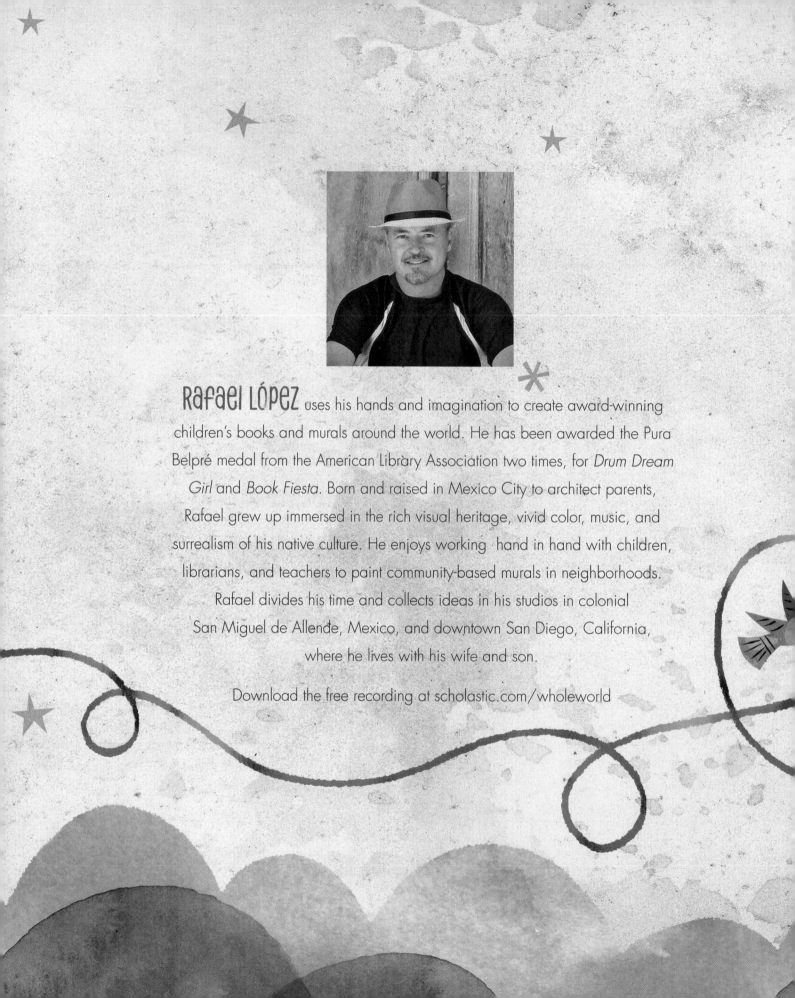

Rafael López uses his hands and imagination to create award-winning children's books and murals around the world. He has been awarded the Pura Belpré medal from the American Library Association two times, for *Drum Dream Girl* and *Book Fiesta*. Born and raised in Mexico City to architect parents, Rafael grew up immersed in the rich visual heritage, vivid color, music, and surrealism of his native culture. He enjoys working hand in hand with children, librarians, and teachers to paint community-based murals in neighborhoods. Rafael divides his time and collects ideas in his studios in colonial San Miguel de Allende, Mexico, and downtown San Diego, California, where he lives with his wife and son.

Download the free recording at scholastic.com/wholeworld